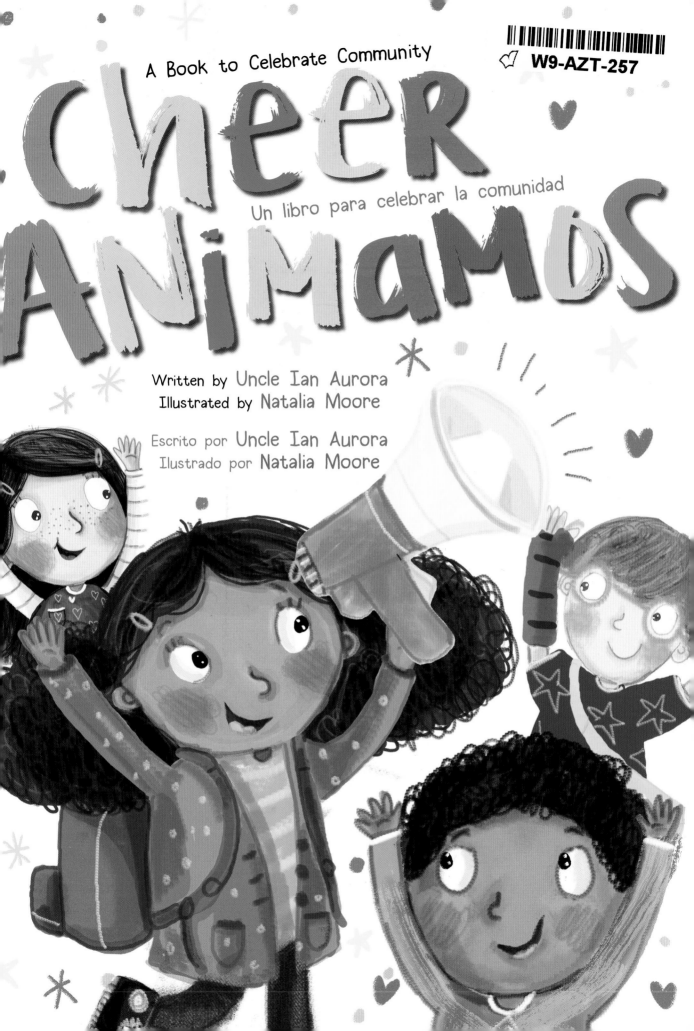

A Book to Celebrate Community

# Cheer
# Animamos

Un libro para celebrar la comunidad

Written by Uncle Ian Aurora
Illustrated by Natalia Moore

Escrito por Uncle Ian Aurora
Ilustrado por Natalia Moore

I want us to CHEER
for the people we know,
the community that helps us
to learn and to grow.
They make our lives better
in so many ways,
so let's CHEER for them all
as we go through our days!

Quiero que ANIMEMOS
a la gente que conocemos,
la comunidad que nos ayuda
a aprender y crecer.
Hacen mejor nuestras vidas de
muchas maneras, así vamos
a ANIMAR a todos ellos
como pasamos nuestros días.

Let's **CHEER** first for moms.
They help us to blossom.

Primero, vamos a **ANIMAR** a las madres. Nos ayudan a florecer.

CHEER for our grandpas.
They make our day
awesome!

Vamos a **ANIMAR** a los abuelos. ¡Hacen nuestro día genial!

CHEER for the grannies...
the abuelas... the nanas!

¡Vamos a **ANIMAR** a las abuelas...
las abuelitas... las yayas!

CHEER for the dads.
They all act bananas!

Vamos a ANIMAR
a los padres. ¡Actúan graciosos!

**CHEER** for our brothers and sisters who are all super cool and the funny bus driver who gets us to school.

Vamos a **ANIMAR** a nuestros hermanos y hermanas que son geniales y el conductor del autobús quien nos lleva a la escuela.

**CHEER** for police, firefighters, and more...

Vamos a **ANIMAR**
a la policía, los bomberos,
y más...

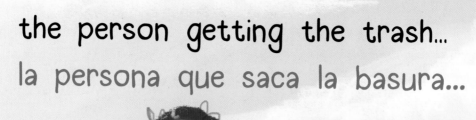

the person getting the trash...
la persona que saca la basura...

the one minding the store.

la persona cuidando la tienda.

CHEER for teachers
who teach us to read

Vamos a **ANIMAR**
a los maestros que
nos enseñan leer

and the librarian who has
every book we might need.

y la bibliotecaria que tiene
cada libro que necesitamos.

and the janitor
who makes
sure the place
doesn't smell.

y el conserje que se asegura de
que la escuela no huela.

CHEER for our pack, for our squad, for our scouts, for our teammates who try extra hard to get outs.

Vamos a **ANIMAR** a nuestros grupitos, los boy scouts y las girl scouts, a nuestros compañeros de equipo que se esfuerzan conseguir los outs.

CHEER for our cousins,
our uncles, and aunts.

Vamos a **ANIMAR**
a nuestros primos,
tíos, y tías.

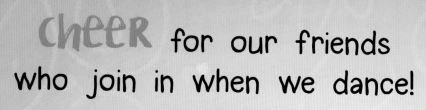

CHEER for our friends
who join in when we dance!

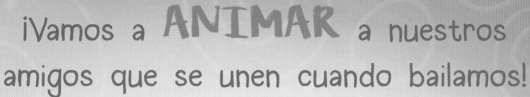

¡Vamos a **ANIMAR** a nuestros
amigos que se unen cuando bailamos!

These are the people we see every day. CHEER for each one with the loudest HOORAY! Working and learning and playing together makes our communities become even better. At the end of the day, no one does it alone, so let's CHEER for them all with a big MEGAPHONE!

Estas son las personas que vemos cada día. ¡ANIMA a cada una con la hurra más fuerte! Trabajar y aprender y jugar juntos hace mejor nuestras comunidades. Al final del día, nadie lo hace solo, así ¡ANIMAMOS a todos ellos con un megáfono gigante!

Now **CHEER** all together
in one big, happy chorus
to say thanks to the author
who wrote this book for us!

Ahora, **¡ANIMAMOS** juntos
en un coro gigante y feliz para
decir gracias al autor que escribió
este libro para nosotros!